S0-BDG-661

AESOP
UP-TO-DATE

AESOP
UP-TO-DATE

BY **Robert L. Zimler**

ILLUSTRATIONS BY **Roy McKie**

Clarkson N. Potter, Inc./Publisher NEW YORK

To my wife and children
without whose constant help
this book would have been written sooner

FOREWORD, INTRODUCTION, AND WARNING

Precisely as the label on a bottle of self-prescribed medicine generally contains a warning to the user, so the following statement is intended to caution the reader:

The author of this book, Professor Duerf, was introduced to me in Vienna three years ago by some friends I was visiting on my vacation. Professor Duerf was a highly regarded psychoanalyst and, by common report, the favorite pupil of Sigmund Freud himself. I do not deny that I was much impressed by the profundity and authority of his professional judgments and completely charmed by the warmth and graciousness of his personal manner.

Having learned that I was a writer, Professor Duerf sought me out privately a day or two before I was to leave Vienna. He explained that he had struggled for many years with the problem of increasing public knowledge of the great insights achieved by psychoanalysis. By an inspiration, he had hit upon the scheme of revising Aesop's Fables for this purpose. "The early Christians rewrote Aesop to help spread their religious teachings," he argued. "Why should the fables not be rewritten now to incorporate the newest discoveries about man's emotional nature?"

His plan possessed one great advantage, he pointed out. As parents would read the new fables to their children, two generations could learn their lesson simultaneously. And so Professor Duerf asked me to take his manuscript to the United States and seek a publisher. Although my only publishing connections related to my own works in mathematics, I was only too glad to agree to further such a meritorious purpose.

Scarcely was I back in this country when I received the most astonishing letter from my friends in Vienna. Professor Duerf had been arrested as a complete humbug and a fraud. He was not a psychoanalyst and even his name was fictitious, being simply "Freud" spelled backwards. Newspaper clippings enclosed with the letter indicated he had taken outrageous emotional and financial advantage of a large number of women patients. After a hurried trial (from which press and public were excluded) on a lurid catalog of counts covering most of Austria's criminal statutes, Professor Duerf was given a sentence of thirty years' imprisonment. The severity of the sentence possibly is explained by a rumor that one of his victims was the wife of a Cabinet member.

I immediately decided to return the manuscript to Professor Duerf together with a terse and dignified note, reading, "I am sure you would not expect me to seek publication of your book under the present circumstances." But the prison authorities refused to permit delivery of the manuscript to Professor Duerf, claiming

6

that prison regulations permitted only brief personal letters to the inmates. (Lately I have learned that the jailers, on receiving and studying the manuscript, decided it was an elaborate code message that they could not quite decipher, but which probably was a plan to help him escape!)

So I placed the manuscript in a file drawer. There the matter rested until a few months ago, when I received a pathetic letter from a young girl of eighteen. She was the illegitimate and only child of Professor Duerf, who had just died in prison. Her sole legacy was the manuscript. Would I not renew my efforts, she pleaded, to have his book published? With the funds she would obtain from the book she intended to come to the United States and become a great actress. (Her enclosed photograph revealed that the unfortunate young lady was possessed of the most exceptional beauty.)

As a way out of my predicament, I submitted the manuscript to several professional authorities. To my astonishment, the experts agreed that these fables should prove beneficial to children and adults alike, unless taken in excessive doses. Accordingly, I felt justified in proceeding to arrange this publication.

I emphasize, however, that if you are seriously ill emotionally or if your psychic distress or discomfort persists, you should discontinue use of this book and consult a qualified practitioner immediately. In that case, you still may console yourself that your purchase of this book has helped finance the dramatic career of a beautiful and warmhearted young girl. This is a lot more than can be said of some other books by admittedly more respectable authors.

ROBERT L. ZIMLER

CONTENTS

1
THE FOX
AND THE GRAPES

A fox and his younger sister came upon a vineyard laden with the ripest and most fragrant grapes they had ever encountered. The grapes, however, were too high on the vines for the foxes to reach.

After much jumping to no avail, the younger fox said, "Those grapes look too sour to eat. I think I'll go home and see what Mother has for lunch. Are you coming?"

Her brother, motivated by sibling rivalry, answered, "No, indeed. You know very well that you are just rationalizing your inability to reach those grapes. But I am a realist and willing to face the facts. Those grapes undoubtedly are more delicious than any we have ever eaten and I shall persist until I have tasted some."

So the younger fox trotted off, but her brother stubbornly continued to leap at the grapes. The more tired he grew and the less successful his efforts, the more he was convinced of the exquisite flavor of the grapes.

The emotional frustration soon induced a nervous breakdown, and the fox began to chase his own tail in a circle, yelping senselessly. Hearing the fox, the farmer who owned the vineyard came out with his shotgun and shot the fox through the head, blowing his brains to smithereens.

MORAL: *If at first you don't succeed, don't try again.*

2
THE PIG
AND THE LION

Threatened by a sudden flood that inundated the forest, a pig managed to save himself by clambering onto a large log floating by. To his consternation, a lion, also intent on saving himself from the flood, joined the pig on the log.

Apprehending his danger, the pig said, "My powerful friend, fate has arranged for us to share this log. May I respectfully suggest that you do not let your appetite get the better of your reason? Our footing here is most precarious, and the smallest struggle is certain to send both of us to the bottom of the river."

"I am impressed with the wisdom of your suggestion," the lion replied. "I certainly shall refrain from trying to eat you, lest it prove our joint undoing."

Pleased by the lion's reply, the pig answered, "Very

well. But try not to forget your prudent resolve when your appetite becomes keener."

So the pig and the lion spent the night peacefully on the log. In the morning, the lion said, "What a strange dream I had! I dreamed that I was visiting in the square of a pleasant town. The people seemed to take no notice of me and I went about freely. Then I observed some people entering a synagogue for their Sabbath worship and, on an impulse, I joined them. Though I did not understand the language of the prayers, the ceremonies were pleasing to me."

The pig smiled to himself but refrained from comment. And though the lion grew hungry as the day wore on, he made no move against the pig.

The following morning, the lion said. "This is most odd. I seem to have continued my dream of the previous night and found myself in the same town square. But on this occasion I overheard some people talking about a special Friday morning service at the old cathedral, so I made a visit there. I greatly enjoyed the services, although I must admit I did not comprehend a single word of the Latin in which they were conducted."

The pig again smiled to himself and maintained his silence. But the lion, growing hungrier as the hours passed, became more irritable toward his companion.

That night he growled in his sleep almost continuously.

When the lion awoke, he said to the pig, "This has never happened to me before! My dream of the previous two nights was resumed last night. I was in the same town once more, but this time I entered a church. I am not quite sure of the denomination, but the services were held in English. I enjoyed this visit most of all those I made in my dreams."

The pig became melancholy on hearing this and said, "I believe the time has come for us to part. So farewell."

"Wait," cried the lion. "I have kept my word and have not threatened your person. Then why should you now abandon the safety of this log?"

The pig answered, "Please understand that I personally have no religious preference or prejudice of any kind. But as Jews never eat pork and as Catholics do not eat meat on Fridays, I am troubled by your conversion to another religion that permits you to eat me at any time. So I am better off now taking my chances with the flood than with your unsatisfied appetite." With this, the pig dove from the log into the river, leaving the lion to cope with his hunger as best he could.

MORAL: *The harder the mattress, the softer the dream.*

3

THE BOY WHO
CRIED, "WOLF!"

As a result of a childhood trauma, a youth was a compulsive liar. His habitual lying made him unreliable at whatever task he was entrusted, so he was finally given the duty of caring for a flock of sheep. But the youth found an excellent opportunity to lie excitingly in his new employment. He shouted "Wolf! Wolf!" at the top of his voice, as if a wolf was attacking his flock.

The villagers promptly responded to his alarm but found no wolf when they arrived. Unabashed, the lying youth berated the villagers. "What took you so long?" he demanded. "I nearly was killed, driving off the wolf by myself."

Again the next day, the young shepherd raised his false cry of "Wolf! Wolf!" and again the villagers came rushing to his help. But when no wolf was to be seen, they were suspicious that the youth was up to his old tricks. However, the youth dissipated their suspicions by saying boldly, "Unless you can make a lot better time coming to my rescue, I'm going to quit. I daily risk my life fighting off ferocious beasts all by myself, while you casually stroll out here, probably stopping now and then to pick flowers or admire the scenic splendors."

Disturbed by this rebuke, the villagers promised to employ greater haste on the next occasion. That very night, a large pack of wolves attacked the villagers' flocks, and from all sides the cries of "Wolf!" were heard. Feeling guilty toward the shepherd who had called them before for aid, the villagers disregarded the cries of the other shepherds and rushed to help only the liar.

The prompt action of the townspeople succeeded in saving both the young shepherd and his flock. But all the other flocks suffered heavily, and one courageous shepherd was bitten badly by the wolves as he defended his charges. He contracted hydrophobia in consequence and died the most painful and horrible death imaginable.

MORAL: *Only the innocent can afford to feel guilty.*

4

THE LION, THE FOX, AND THE STAG

Having grown too feeble to hunt, an aged lion lay weak and starving in his den when a fox chanced to pass by. "Friend fox," called out the desperate lion, "if you are as clever as you are reputed to be, perhaps you can lure some game within my reach. Instead of trapping stray mice and pilfering birds' nests, you shall share equally in the spoils and eat your fill."

Nothing loath to be a partner of the lion, the fox said, "It certainly will not be simple, but I am content to try." So the fox went into the forest to seek a dupe.

Encountering a stag admiring his own reflection as he drank from a stream, the fox considered he had found a suitable candidate. "I bring you great news," said the clever fox to the stag. "The king of beasts, the lion, lies dying and has sent me to inform you that he has chosen you his successor."

Suspicious of the fox, the stag said, "You are a clever rascal and only up to some trick or other, I warrant."

Pretending to be angered by this, the fox answered, "The lion has made a poor choice, I see. You must be stupid if you do not realize the lion could not choose otherwise."

"That is true," said the stag, and proudly tossed his antlers. "I am widely respected for my beauty, wisdom, and character. My very appearance is regal. You are right, the lion had no other choice but to select me."

"Then you must hasten to the lion," urged the fox, "so that he may officially designate you to rule after him. Follow me."

Unsuspecting, the stag followed at the heels of the fox, who led him into the lion's den. There the lion sprang at the stag, but because of his infirmity, he only succeeded in scratching the stag's ears before the stag broke from the lion's grasp. Terrified, the animal fled and did not stop until he found refuge deep in the forest.

The fox began berating the lion for his clumsy failure, but the lion said, "I am humiliated enough by my own weakness without the addition of your words. Instead of upbraiding me, you would do better to entice the stag into my reach again."

"After the stag's experience here, that is all but impossible," replied the fox. "However, I shall do what I can."

Finding the stag's trail, the fox came upon the wounded animal hiding in a thicket but acted as if he were bound elsewhere. "How fortunate the lion discovered you were a coward before he made you king," said the fox. "I am on my way to notify the bear that he will be the lion's successor."

"What!" exclaimed the stag. "You trickster, you dare to call me coward because I would not stay to be eaten!"

Hearing this, the fox pretended to be convulsed with merriment. Then he said, "The lion only took your head between his paws to whisper with his dying breath his blessings on you. But your cowardice has cost you the throne."

"I misunderstood the gesture," said the stag. "It is certainly not right of the lion to choose another in my place without giving me a chance to explain. It's not that I care about the honor, but the bear would make an ill-mannered king."

"What you say is persuasive," said the fox, "but it's no use talking to me about it. I am only the lion's messenger and do what I am bidden."

"Do me the favor of obtaining an audience with the lion for me," pleaded the stag. "I shall apologize and perhaps can prevail upon him to keep his original intention."

"The lion will be angry that I have not performed his errand to the bear, but I like to see justice done," said the fox. "Come, I will return with you to the lion."

So the stag willingly went into the lion's den again. That night, as the lion and the fox chewed the stag's bones, they laughed heartily at the stag's opinion of himself.

MORAL: *Repeat your mistakes; at least you'll know what to expect.*

5

ZEUS AND
THE SPIDER

A little spider went before Zeus to make a complaint. "My sexual instincts urge me," the spider said, "to seek a mate. But I have noticed that our females invariably dine upon us after mating. While mating may be a pleasant form of suicide, couldn't a more friendly and permanent social relationship between the sexes be devised for us?"

The god, impressed by the little creature's courage in coming before him, was disposed to remedy the spider's grievance, especially because it was Zeus's wife, Hera, who had thought up this spiteful idea as a warning to Zeus. "You may borrow the instinct of another species in place of your own," said Zeus. "But choose wisely what you wish for yourself and your fellows. Even I cannot alter instincts whenever I wish."

Cautioned by Zeus's remarks, the spider said, "Per-

haps I could benefit from some frank discussions with other creatures." So the spider went forth to seek counsel from all he might meet.

Encountering a bee gathering nectar, the spider begged some information about the bee's experience. "In my species," replied the bee, "sex is a privilege reserved only for royalty and some lazy shirkers. And as we put our males to death, while the queen herself slaughters her sisters at birth, the possession of sex seems to be fatal. You're better off without sex, particularly if you want to keep your mind on your work, like me."

"I have wasted my time, questioning only a fellow insect," thought the spider. "Sex seems a complicated instinct, probably requiring the guidance of intelligence. I'd best talk with a creature who possesses a brain, however small."

Coming to a stream, the spider spied a salmon and asked for the fish's views. "Sex must be wonderful," said the salmon. "Why else should all my ancestors have died for it? But until I myself swim upstream to the falls, never to return, I can tell you nothing from my own personal knowledge."

Dissatisfied, the spider continued on his way and met a rooster. "I daresay my hens may find sex to their liking," said the rooster. "But sex demands too much of me. While I am permitted as many wives as I can find, a young rooster can win a mate only by fighting me to the death. So I live from minute to minute, always in fear of losing my life and my loves together."

Wearying of his useless travels, the spider returned to the throne of Zeus. "It seems," reported the spider, "that wherever sex is, death is just around the corner. And as it hardly matters to me whether I die eaten or beaten, I am content to keep my instincts as they are."

Taking his leave of Zeus, the spider sought out a pleasing mate, wooed her, won her, and willingly became her supper.

MORAL: *Sex and justice are both blind.*

6

THE LION
AND THE MOUSE

A lion of normal egoistic tendencies was captured by a party of hunters and bound with heavy ropes. A little mouse was attracted by the roars of the outraged lion.

Taking great pride in his willingness to help others, in spite of his puniness, the mouse asked in a sympathetic tone, "Does something hurt you? Can I be of any service?"

"Go ask questions elsewhere," snarled the lion. "I've got enough trouble without engaging in small talk with rodents."

"What is the difficulty?" persisted the mouse, not offended by the lion's rudeness. "I enjoy helping others."

"You must be as blind as you are stupid," said the lion angrily. "Here I am, helplessly tied up and awaiting removal to some zoo, where I am to be caged for the rest of my life. And if I am unable to free myself, with all my great strength, then how can you be so idiotic as to volunteer your assistance?"

"If that is all," replied the mouse warmly, "then stop worrying. I shall chew through your ropes immediately."

At the cost of several broken incisors, the mouse succeeded after a while in gnawing through one rope, enabling the lion to free himself from his remaining bonds.

"My friend!" bellowed the lion. "You saved my life and I am not going to forget it. Come with me and you shall live in ease forevermore."

"It was nothing, really," said the mouse graciously.

But the lion begged, "At least permit my family to thank you." When the mouse assented, the lion placed the mouse carefully in the softest part of his mane and bounded off into the forest.

The lion's family was overjoyed by his return and immediately gave a big party, at which the mouse was the guest of honor. Unfortunately, the mouse drank a thimbleful of fermented coconut juice and began to brag. He went from guest to guest, saying, "You see that lout? With all his brute strength, he could not save himself and was trembling in terror. But I untied him and he owes his very life to me."

Hearing this, and without even thinking the matter over twice, the lion lifted his powerful paw, squashed his benefactor flatter than a pancake, and flicked his corpse into the shrubbery for the ants.

MORAL: *Be grateful to those who accept your favors.*

7

THE BEE
AND THE
HUMMINGBIRD

A hummingbird and a bee got into a dispute over which was the first to discover a flower-laden bush and consequently entitled to dine on the nectar. Losing patience, the bee bared his stinger and sought to plunge his weapon into his adversary.

"Foolish insect," said the hummingbird as he dodged the bee. "To sting me will cause your own death. What good will nectar be to you then?"

Halting his efforts, the bee asked the bird, "Death? What is that?"

Astounded to learn that the bee was ignorant of the subject, the bird answered, "You should understand that death means you can never enjoy again the sight or scent of flowers, sip nectar, or buzz with other bees. You will be unable to fly, crawl, or even wiggle your antennae. Your legs, wings, and body will turn brittle, eventually to be blown away by the wind. Were you really ignorant of all this?"

"Horrible, horrible," said the bee, shuddering, and flew in terror to its hive, leaving the bush to the possession of the hummingbird. For several days, the bee huddled in a cranny of the hive, neither eating nor communicating with its fellows but only trembling over its narrow escape from death.

Realizing, however, that in its first shock it had failed to learn enough about death, the bee finally left its hive and went to seek out the hummingbird. When the bee encountered its teacher, the bee said, "I have been greatly disturbed by the information you disclosed about death. But I forgot to ask, will death come for me even if I do not use my stinger?"

The hummingbird laughed and said, "You are just suffering from the shock that all creatures experience when they first learn they are not immortal."

"But is death my certain fate?" asked the bee.

"Of course," snapped the hummingbird, irritated by the foolish question. "And you have no way of foretelling

how horrible your death may be. You may be swallowed whole and in one gulp by the scissor-tailed flycatcher as he darts gracefully through the evening air. A hunting wasp may paralyze you and plant its eggs on your body, so that its young will eat you alive. And it is not even improbable you accidentally will absorb a few particles of DDT intended for a less useful insect and will die in all the pain your rudimentary nervous system can express."

"If you are not just making up stories for the fun of seeing me turn pale," replied the bee, "then my death can serve no purpose unless I have used my stinger in defense of the interests of myself or my species."

"True and aptly put," said the hummingbird, whereupon the bee plunged its stinger into the bird's jugular vein and died happily.

MORAL: *Your means should justify your end.*

8

THE RAT
AND THE FROG

A shy, introverted land rat struck up a chance friendship with an extroverted frog. The frog had mild sadistic tendencies, usually expressed in practical jokes at the expense of his friends. Nevertheless, the rat valued his friendship with the frog, for the outgoing frog knew everyone, went everywhere, and always kept things moving at a lively pace.

One day the frog suggested to the rat that they should tie their feet together as an expression of their friendship. This sentimental idea brought tears to the rat's eyes and he readily agreed.

Fastened to each other, the rat and the frog ate their dinner together in a wheat field and experienced no special difficulty. But after dinner, they went for a walk and passed a pond. The frog jumped in, dragging his friend with him. The rat drowned immediately.

"What a dull creature that rat was!" said the frog. "He always managed to take the fun out of my plans." And the frog began to untie himself from his dead companion.

While the frog was thus engaged, he unfortunately attracted the attention of a hawk circling in the sky. Encumbered by his victim, the frog was unable to escape the hawk, who enjoyed a two-course dinner for a change.

MORAL: *Opposites attract only trouble.*

9

THE CROW
AND THE FOX

An old crow, so ugly she had never been able to find a mate, was sitting in a tree eating a piece of stolen cheese. A passing fox spied the crow and desired the cheese. So the fox called up to the crow, "You are so homely that it seems altogether likely to me you have some compensating virtue. Could it be your voice? If you'd care to let me hear a few notes, I am something of an expert and will give you my unbiased opinion."

This offer of a musical audition was both novel and pleasing to the crow. She opened her beak to sing, letting the cheese fall to the ground. The fox instantly snatched up the cheese and ran off into the forest to eat it at his leisure.

"How thoughtless of me," said the crow to herself, "to sing without first feeding my guest. Who can listen to music on an empty stomach? If I apologize, perhaps the fox will be kind enough to grant me another opportunity."

So the crow composed a sincere letter of apology to the fox, concluding with an invitation to a supper-musicale. When the fox accepted, the crow was careful to feed him to bursting before beginning her songs. Pleased by his free meal, the fox applauded and even insisted on several encores.

Thereafter the crow regularly gave supper-musicales for the fox. Not only did the constant practice actually improve her voice, but her personality changed as well. She acquired so much poise, assurance, and self-confidence that she put on airs. This entranced an old bachelor crow who, in spite of her homeliness, proposed to her and married her.

MORAL: *The cheapest virtue is telling the truth.*

10
THE CAGED BIRD

A boy caught a bird singing in the meadow, brought it home and kept it in a cage at the window. During the day the bird remained silent, but at night he sang. An owl who heard the bird singing asked him why he only sang at night. "It was my singing during the day that attracted the boy who caught me and caged me," said the bird. "So I've learned my lesson and sing only at night."

"A wise precaution, had you taken it before," replied the owl.

MORAL: *Save some sorrow, there'll be troubles to-morrow.*

11

THE LION
AND THE DOE

An aging lion, unable to depend any longer on fleetness and strength to bring down game for himself, thought to obtain his prey by cunning instead. Selecting a plump young doe as his victim, the lion boldly approached her while she was feeding.

When the doe saw the lion approaching she prepared to flee, but the lion called out, "Hold on, this is only a social call. I merely wish to meet you as a friend."

"Very well," answered the wary doe, "but keep your distance."

Remaining where he was, the lion continued, "I have come to extend an invitation. I'd like to have you for dinner at my den this evening."

"You are kind," replied the doe. "But our diet is very different. I enjoy salads while you prefer flesh."

"True," said the lion, "but I am ready to serve you with herbs."

"I already have an engagement for this evening," said the doe.

Slavering with hunger, the lion said, "Very well, I can dine on the marrow."

"I think you meant to say 'morrow,'" said the doe.

"Pray excuse the slip of the tongue," said the eager lion.

"Unfortunately," said the doe to the lion as she trotted off, "I feel in my bones that I'd best dine by myself."

MORAL: *It takes a lot of planning to tell a lie.*

12

THE TORTOISE
AND THE HARE

An atypical tortoise, much given to aggressive and boastful behavior, challenged a hare to a race. The hare only laughed at the tortoise for his conceit. But when the tortoise persisted in taunting the hare that he feared the outcome, the hare consented.

An owl was selected to be the impartial judge, a course was laid out, and all the small creatures gathered to witness the match. When the starting signal was given, the hare was off like an arrow, while the tortoise inched forward on his laborious way.

Seeing the tortoise left far behind, the hare considered his victory certain and stopped to rest under a shady tree, where he soon fell asleep. When the hare awoke, he saw that the tortoise still was nowhere in sight, so he took a leisurely lunch. While gathering some berries for dessert, the hare encountered a rather pretty doe of his species with whom he struck up a pleasant conversation.

Meanwhile the tortoise had continued plodding along without rest or interruption. And late that evening, while the hare was engaged in advancing his flirtation with the doe to an intensely active courtship, the tortoise crossed the finish line. Before all the animals, the owl declared the tortoise to be the official winner.

Pleased by his success, the tortoise asked the animals to make him their messenger in place of the hare. But the animals only said, "Are you stupid or something? Everybody but you knows that the hare can run faster than you whenever he wants to."

MORAL: *He who can doesn't have to.*

13
THE KANGAROO
AND HER
INFANT

A mother kangaroo, unaware that her mate had been dispatched by a party of hunters, concluded that he had deserted her. Embittered by this supposed infidelity, the kangaroo declared to her baby, "You poor child, your father is worthless, lacking alike in regard for me and love for you. Let him take what pleasure he can in a younger and more winsome consort. We have each other and I shall be father and mother to you."

So the kangaroo gave herself over completely to the care of her infant. For a while she permitted him to play with the other little kangaroos, but after he received a few playful thumps, she thought it best to keep him in her pouch a while longer. Even as he grew older, she did not require him to forage for his own food but instead she still transported him from shrub to shrub so he could nibble his meals from his perch in her pouch. The kangaroo became quite content with his lot, was very devoted to his mother, and showed no interest in even the most agile girl kangaroos.

The strain of carrying a full-grown kangaroo in her pouch, however, caused the mother to suffer a fatal rupture. Grief-stricken and unable to fend for himself, her son died of starvation a few days later.

MORAL: *Leave a little room between the womb and the tomb.*

14

THE WOODSMAN
AND HIS WIFE

From his throne on Mount Olympus, Zeus observed a woodsman on a stormy winter night searching frantically in a forest with the aid of a lamp. Curious, the god disguised himself as a traveler and descended to earth to learn the woodsman's purpose.

"My journey requires me to be abroad," said the disguised god to the woodsman, "but why should you be out freezing your bones at this late hour?"

"My stupid lump of a wife has lost her wedding band somewhere about," answered the woodsman. "As it is made of gold, I cannot bear its loss but must search until it is found."

"But are you not fearful of leaving your wife alone on such a dreadful night as this?" asked Zeus.

"Oh, the shepherd who keeps his flock near my hut was good enough to agree to keep my wife company until my return," said the woodsman cheerfully.

"Hasten home, my friend," counseled the god. "You search here for a bauble that will remain until morning, while at home you risk losing something of far greater worth."

"You judge me carelessly," replied the woodsman. "I am only a poor woodsman and possess nothing of greater value than the ring unless it be my ax." So Zeus returned to Mount Olympus and the woodsman resumed his search. At dawn, the man discovered the wedding ring and returned home, where he was happy to find his ax still safe in its customary place.

MORAL: *Accidents seldom happen.*

15

THE FOX WHO
LOST HIS TAIL

A fox once was caught in a trap. He struggled desperately to free himself and finally did so, but only at the cost of leaving his tail behind him. He hid in a lonely cave while he recovered from his traumatic amputation, but, even after his wound had healed, he was reluctant to return to the company of his fellow foxes.

"They will sneer at me for not having a tail," thought the fox to himself. "As long as they have tails and I do not, my life will be miserable. There's an angle here somewhere, if I put my mind to it."

After much consideration, the fox devised a plan and boldly trotted back to rejoin his companions.

"Where have you been?" the foxes asked as soon as they saw their companion.

"To the plastic surgeon," replied the fox, and turned around to let them see that his tail had been removed.

"It was very expensive and I must admit it was painful, too, but I'm glad I had enough courage to go through it."

When the other foxes demanded to know why he had submitted to such an unheard-of operation, the fox said cunningly, "A tail is a useless and old-fashioned append-age, completely out of style. It makes you hotter in summer and colder in winter. It is a refuge for every homeless louse, tick, and mite. Most important, a tail slows you up when you're running for your life while providing hunters and dogs a convenient handle for catching you. In a word, tails are unsightly, unsanitary, and a hazard to life."

Moved by this reasoning, all the foxes at once agreed to cut off their tails also. But an old fox spoke up, say-ing, "Everything you have told us may be true. But will our females like us without tails?"

This made the foxes change their minds and they retained their tails.

MORAL: *Even sex requires some display advertising.*

16
THE SUN
AND THE WIND

The sun, who took pride in his pleasant disposition, got into an argument with the north wind, who took equal pride in his opposite nature. The sun boasted that the genial warmth of his personality won him respect from all, but the north wind claimed that he received greater homage by virtue of his stormy temper.

To settle the quarrel, the sun proposed a contest to see which could induce a farmer working in his field to remove his cloak. The north wind agreed and took his turn first. He hurled icy blasts against the farmer, but the more he blew, the more tightly the farmer pulled his cloak against himself.

When it was the sun's turn, he sent a shower of his warmest rays down on the farmer. "Strange weather we're having," grumbled the farmer, and removed his cloak, thus giving the victory to the sun.

The sun laughed cheerfully over the outcome, but the wind said, "Hold on a moment. You've beaten me fairly, but now let us see who can make the farmer don his cloak again."

"You are a bad sport and a poor loser," said the confident sun, "but I do not mind another contest."

The sun directed more of his beams at the farmer. But the perspiring farmer only removed his shirt and went on with his work.

Then the wind had his chance again and blew a few freezing gusts. "I can't remember as changeable a spring as this," said the shivering farmer. He hastily replaced his shirt and cloak, making the north wind the winner.

The sun was greatly displeased at being bested, but, remembering his bragging about his good nature, he said nothing. This repression caused the sun to break out the very next day in a psychosomatic rash of gigantic sunspots.

MORAL: *The best way to gain from your temper is to lose it.*

17

THE LION, THE JACKAL, AND THE FOX

Contrary to the usual ways of their kind, a lion and a jackal became the best of friends. And when a serious illness overtook the lion, his friend, the jackal, was greatly disturbed. The jackal hurried to all the animals to inform them that the lion was gravely ill and required that they should come to visit, not forgetting to bring suitable gifts.

All the creatures of the forest, great and small, heeded the jackal and called upon the lion to express their concern. The fox alone failed to put in an appearance. The jackal was irate. "Even if the fox does not care what befalls you," said the jackal to the lion, "still he should present himself because of the courtesy due the king of animals. The fox has insulted you grievously."

The lion, of course, failed to sense that the jackal's

excessive concern actually betrayed a subconscious resentment of the lion. Nor did the lion appreciate that the jackal's malice was directed less against the welfare of the fox than the lion's peace of mind. So the lion, angered at the fox, directed the jackal to bring the fox before him.

When the fox appeared and saw how matters stood, he said, "I'm sorry to be so late in getting here, but I've been exerting myself rather strenuously on your behalf. I'm not the kind, you understand, to express my sympathy merely with words or convey my respects with a trifling gift. No, I've been running from doctor to doctor seeking a remedy for your sickness. When the jackal came for me, I already was hurrying here to report my success."

"My thoughtful friend!" thundered the overjoyed lion. "Now describe the cure to me at once. There's not a moment to be lost if I am to recover."

"Well, it may sound peculiar, but this specialist claimed it never fails," replied the fox. "It's very simple. You just cook a fresh jackal and drink the broth, every drop."

Without the slightest heed for the jackal's protests about their years of friendship, the lion immediately boiled the jackal alive.

MORAL: *A friend is an enemy who hasn't made his move yet.*

18

THE CRICKET
AND THE ANT

A cricket, having neglected to lay up a store of food for itself during the summer and autumn, was hungry when the winter came. So the cricket went to an ant nest to beg food from the ants' supply.

The ant who guarded the entrance to the nest sought to turn the cricket away. "You would not be starving now if you had worked like us," said the ant. "But you laughed at those who were industrious and wasted your own time in noisy fiddling."

"Refuse me charity, if you wish," said the cricket. "But pray do not seek to pass judgment on my musicianship. What sounds like only a single chirp to you is a flawless rendition by me of three violin slurs, each lasting a fiftieth of a second in duration and separated by silent intervals or rests of similarly brief duration. Playing in an octave pitched one step above piano range, I complete the entire performance without error in a total time of one-tenth of a second."

"You may be a virtuoso," answered the ant, "but of what use to you is your music? You would have done better to employ your time gathering grains of wheat and barley."

"I have succeeded in combining with my music a unique system of scientific observation and measurement," continued the cricket. "If anyone wishes to know the temperature he merely has to count the number of chirps I play in one minute, divide that number by four, then add forty—and, behold, that is the temperature expressed in degrees Fahrenheit."

"Very ingenious," answered the ant, "but how does broadcasting weather reports help feed you?"

"Can you boast of any accomplishment," asked the cricket angrily, "besides amassing a store of food for your own selfish needs?"

Angered in turn, the ant said, "You are a foolish individualist, seeking only pleasure and knowledge. But we ants are the equal, if not the superior, of mankind, the lords of creation. We are more populous than man, our social order is as complex and our ancestry goes back longer. We cultivated underground farms and milked herds of aphid-cattle while men still shivered in caves without fire."

"Anyone can obey an instinct," said the cricket. "You do yourself too much honor, comparing yourselves to men. Men can think."

"We equal mankind there, too," said the ant. "Only we ants, of all living creatures, rival man in regularly waging war against our own species, destroying ourselves more numerously than any natural enemy we possess. Why, we even make slaves of our own kind when their color is different than our own. Has man

54

invented for himself anything greater than war and slavery?"

Abashed by this irrefutable argument, the cricket departed. Soon after, when he died of cold and hunger, the ants found his body, dragged it to their nest and ate it with satisfaction.

MORAL: *When winter comes, spring is far behind.*

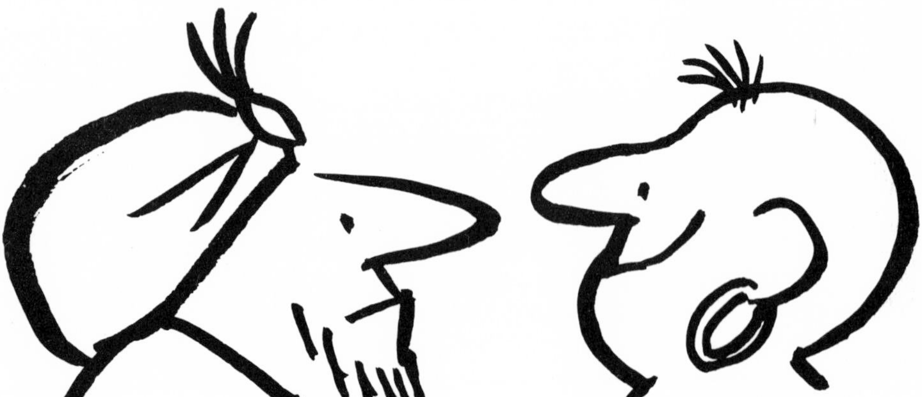

19
THE DOG IN THE MANGER

A young nobleman of the Sultan's court accidentally obtained a glimpse of the youngest and most beautiful of his Sultan's wives and immediately fell in love with her. By much planning he contrived an audience with the wife, but was discovered by the eunuch who was custodian of the harem.

"Before you call the guards," said the nobleman to the eunuch, "would you like to have this ring?" And the nobleman offered the eunuch the large ruby ring on his finger.

"I am faithful to my trust," said the eunuch staunchly.

The nobleman then sought to appeal to the eunuch's better nature. "The Sultan undoubtedly will have me boiled in oil," said the nobleman. "It is a very unpleasant way for a young man to die. Would you wish to bear my death on your conscience?"

"You have nobody to blame but yourself," replied the eunuch unfeelingly.

Seeking to minimize his misdeed, the nobleman said, "The woman is no good to you and only rarely to the Sultan. Should I be punished for desiring what is otherwise wasted?"

Angered by this argument, the eunuch summoned the guards, who dragged the unfortunate nobleman before the Sultan. When the Sultan heard the case, he sighed and said, "Ah, what I would not do to be young again and care enough for a woman to risk my life for her." Then, softened by the memory of his own youthful daring, the Sultan set the nobleman free, bestowed the erring wife upon him as a gift, and sent him to rule one of his finest but most distant provinces.

But the eunuch was so enraged by the Sultan's sentimental leniency that he immediately resigned his job at the harem. He opened a bazaar-stall, where he sold perfumes, ointments and love potions to the women of the city and soon became as wealthy as the Sultan himself.

MORAL: *It's pretty cozy in a manger.*

20
THE WOLF
AND THE ASS

An ass grazing in a meadow was terrified to observe that a wolf had managed to sneak up close to him. The quick-witted ass did not show that he had discovered the approach of the wolf, but instead hobbled about, pretending to be lame and unable to run.

So the wolf came out of hiding and went up to the ass, meaning to kill it. "Why do you not run?" asked the wolf. "Are you not afraid of being eaten?"

"I'd run soon enough," answered the ass, "but I have gotten a large thorn deep into my foot. It is so painful that I dare not put any weight on it. You would do well to remove the thorn before you eat me, for it is certain to scratch your throat."

"Lift your foot," ordered the wolf and put his head beside the ass's uplifted hoof to see the thorn. Thus favorably situated, the ass kicked the wolf in the head with all its might, killing him outright.

MORAL: *There aren't many Samaritans left around here any more.*

21

THE WOODSMAN WHO LOST HIS AX

Engaged in cutting wood on the bank of a river, a woodcutter took too powerful a stroke, and the ax, flying from his hand, flew off into the river. Being too poor to buy another ax, the man was overcome by his ill fortune and began to weep for the lost tool by which he earned his livelihood.

The god Hermes appeared at the river bank and asked the man the cause of his sorrow. Moved by the simple fellow's tearful answer, Hermes jumped into the river and brought up an ax made of gold. "Rejoice," said Hermes, "I have retrieved your ax."

"No," said the honest woodcutter, "that ax is made of gold, and is not nearly as good as my own. The blade is too soft to chop down even a pine tree, let alone a sturdy oak."

Hermes dived into the river again, but this time returned with an ax made of silver. "Here's your ax," said the god, "I trust you are satisfied now."

"That's not mine, either," replied the man. "Mine was made of iron and had a sharper edge."

So Hermes descended into the water once more and fetched up the woodcutter's own ax.

"Yes, that's it," said the delighted woodcutter, and thanked the god with heartfelt gratitude.

Pleased with the man's character, Hermes said, "Honesty should be rewarded. I give you the gold ax and the silver ax also, to keep as your own."

Overjoyed, the fellow ran home to show his wife his three axes and to tell his neighbors of his fortunate encounter with Hermes. One of the neighbors, hearing the story and thinking to make himself wealthy, went to the

river and threw his ax into the stream. Then he sat down and pretended to weep.

In a twinkling, Hermes appeared before the man. "I have lost the ax by which I feed my wife and my little ones. Take pity and restore my ax," the trickster pleaded.

Realizing he had created a precedent that could keep him busy retrieving or repairing axes for every careless woodcutter in Greece, to the detriment of his duties and recreations on Mount Olympus, the god said rudely, "Heaven helps those who help themselves. And judging by your appearance, a good bath in the river while you search for your ax would not serve you amiss."

MORAL: *Honesty is only ignorance of opportunity.*

22

THE DEER
WITH ONE EYE

As the result of a wound from a hunter's arrow, a deer became blind in one eye. "I shall graze at the seashore," said the deer to himself, "for I can keep my blind eye toward the water while taking good care to watch the forest with my remaining eye." So the deer went to graze at the seashore, keeping watch only over the forest.

But some fishermen in a boat, who noticed the deer, immediately turned their vessel toward shore. They approached the deer from its blind side without difficulty and had venison for their supper that night instead of herring.

MORAL: *He who runs away is caught another day.*

23

THE WOLF AND
THE BABY LAMB

A starving wolf came upon a baby lamb drinking from a river. Burdened by guilt feelings, the wolf sought some justification for devouring the lamb.

So the wolf accused the lamb of muddying the water, making it too foul for the wolf to drink. "That cannot be," said the lamb with the insensitive arrogance of the innocent. "I am below you in the stream and the water is flowing from you to me."

"Well," said the wolf, "you show no respect for the dead. Last year you insulted my father when he was shot by a hunter."

Instead of taking to his heels, the lamb continued to argue like an idiot. "You are mistaken, I wasn't even born last year," said the lamb indignantly.

"You graze on the commons with the other sheep, so clearly you are a Communist subverting our most revered institutions of private ownership," said the wolf, now in a genuine rage.

"My father and mother are members of the Birch Society and I intend to join as soon as I am old enough," bleated the lamb proudly.

"I can't stand a self-righteous hypocrite," said the wolf. "The world is better off without such smug creatures as you." He jumped on the lamb, ate it completely, and did not suffer even the tiniest pang of psychosomatic indigestion.

MORAL: *Reasons are what we tell others in order to deceive ourselves.*

24

THE SHEPHERD
AND THE WOLF
CUBS

On a rocky mountainside, a shepherd came across a litter of wolf cubs whose mother had been killed. The shepherd decided to rear the cubs, hoping he could teach them to guard his sheep.

He fed the little wolves well and, displaying the greatest persistence, sought to train them to obey his commands. If they worried the sheep he beat them, but when they behaved well he fed them tidbits. After many months of effort, the shepherd believed that his patient training had been rewarded.

Accordingly, the shepherd left his flock in the care of the wolves while he went to town to find a buyer for his new breed of sheep dogs. But when he returned with several interested villagers, it was to discover, alas, that the wolves had taken advantage of his absence to kill all the sheep.

MORAL: *If you lead a horse to water, he'll drink.*

25

THE SCULPTOR
AND APHRODITE

A sculptor created a statue of a woman so beautiful that he at once fell in love with it. He gave up all other pursuits and sat before his statue, gazing at it all day and night with anguished passion. Realizing he could never again be content with any mortal woman, he prayed to Aphrodite, Goddess of Love, to transform the marble form into a living person.

Taking pity on the despairing lover, the sentimental goddess granted his prayer and gave life to the statue. The sculptor was ecstatic in his joy and offered unceasing prayers of deepest thankfulness to Aphrodite.

But the sculptor found it was the most difficult of tasks to preserve in the woman the beauty he had created in the statue. "You must remain indoors," he ordered the object of his worship. "The marble pallor of your cheeks might be tanned by the warm beams of the sun, and the

evening wind may roughen the fine texture which I
bestowed upon your skin."

If this were not enough, he barely permitted the
woman to eat or drink. "Enough of food," he would
exclaim as soon as the poor girl had tasted a morsel.
"Are you a pig I sculpted or the most beautiful woman
seen by human eyes? Would you desire to fatten yourself and destroy the perfect symmetry, the harmonious
proportions, the exquisite grace with which my genius
has endowed you?"

Nor was the sculptor reluctant to sacrifice his own
comfort for the preservation of the beauty he had
created. He would not permit the girl to peel potatoes,
wash dishes, or scrub floors, performing these and all
the other chores of the household himself.

Under these conditions, the woman soon found that
living with her creator brought her no joy. So she prayed
to Aphrodite, "It is not me whom the sculptor loves but
only his own handiwork. Then let me be a statue as I
was before." Aphrodite wisely granted this wish, greatly
to the relief of both parties.

MORAL: *It's easier to carve on marble than chisel on
love.*

26

THE SOLDIER
AND THE WAR HORSE

An Athenian soldier, proud of the horse that carried him into battle and kept him safe by reason of its speed and strength, took excellent care of the animal. He would not eat his own supper until he had first fed the horse an ample portion of barley and all the water it needed. He groomed the horse daily and never failed to put salves on its sores.

When the campaign was over, however, the man put the horse to work in his field. It was made to draw a

plough, haul away large rocks, and pull a heavy wagon. But in spite of its hard work, the horse was fed only on chaff and straw.

War broke out again, so the man armed himself and mounted his horse once more. But the exhausted animal could not gallop, and stumbled at every step. When the man rebuked the horse, it said, "If you expected me to behave like a war horse, why did you treat me like a farm donkey?"

MORAL: *Never tell your mistress what you spend on your wife.*

27

THE EAGER
BEAVER

An eager, idealistic, and well-toothed beaver got married. For the sake of his newly acquired bride he did his utmost to get along with his mother-in-law, even though she was the most unpleasant beaver in the entire colony. In spite of his sincere efforts, however, his mother-in-law gave no sign of relenting her ways. She took every opportunity to criticize the beaver in front of others and to report to her daughter any little faults that she might not yet have discovered for herself. Whenever there was the slightest disagreement between the beaver and his wife, the mother-in-law immediately pleaded with her daughter to leave the beaver and not throw her life away on a good-for-nothing.

One day the beaver caught a bad cold that confined him to his lodge, and although his mate was very reluctant to leave him, she was required to work on an emergency dam repair. "I'd best ask my mother to drop in and look after you," said the worried wife.

Hearing this, the beaver begged to be allowed to suffer his illness in solitude. But his mate said, "I don't know why you feel that way about my mother. She's really very fond of you, and it's about time you made up your mind to get along with her." So she arranged for her mother to care for her husband.

As soon as the mother-in-law entered the beaver's lodge, she said, "Such a loafer! Your wife is working with all the other young beavers to repair the dam while you lie here in comfort." But when she took the beaver's temperature, she said, "Oh, you are really sick. I'll rub your chest, you poor boy, with juniper juice, which will relieve the congestion. You needn't be embarrassed. After all, I'm your mother-in-law."

So the beaver let his mother-in-law rub his chest with juniper juice. He was not sure at first, but he soon realized that somehow the nursing care was turning into a seduction. Arguing with himself that it was too late and too scandalous to shout for help, but also flattered by the ardor he had aroused in the old girl, the beaver submitted to his mother-in-law's advances. His cold lasted a full ten days, during which time his mother-in-law continued to look after him.

After he recovered, he and his mother-in-law were the best of friends. While the wife—and the father-in-law, too—never quite understood the basis of the warm friendship, the wife felt in her bones that the whole thing was unnatural and often wished her husband didn't get along so well with her mother.

MORAL: *Hate your mother-in-law and keep two families happy.*

28

THE FROGS WHO WANTED A KING

Living in a pleasant pond, some frogs were nevertheless emotionally insecure because they had no father image. So they elected a committee that went to Zeus to implore his assistance in finding a king.

Meaning well by the frogs, Zeus dropped a large log into the pond and said, "The log shall be your ruler. Respect him and you shall live in peace." At first, the frogs were pleased, for the log provided a convenient place where they could bask in the sun. Moreover, many grubs, beetles, and worms were attracted by the log, which thus increased the frogs' food supply.

However, as the log did not move or speak, the young frogs sneered at it and grew disrespectful. When the log remained indifferent to this rudeness, the frogs felt guilty that they were not punished for this disrespect, which made them even angrier against the log.

So once more the committee of frogs went to Zeus to report their grievance. Vexed by the frogs' dissatisfaction with his judgment, Zeus decided to punish them by sending a huge water snake to their pond.

The snake had a tremendous appetite and lived exclusively on a diet of frogs, eating as many as he could catch. Although the frogs were soon consumed by the snake, they all went to their death happily.

MORAL: *You can't expect frogs to be smarter than people.*

29

THE OAK
AND THE REEDS

An oak tree was boasting of his great strength and sneered at some nearby reeds because they were accustomed to bow before even the lightest breeze. But as the oak was describing the magnificent rigidity of his trunk and the immense depth of his roots, a violent wind suddenly arose. Unyielding to the storm, the powerful oak was blown down and its roots torn from the earth.

Just as the reeds were beginning to brag among themselves how they had survived the oak, some children who had been attracted by the uprooted tree came to play. The children ripped up handfuls of reeds for sport and flung them about, leaving them to die in the sun.

MORAL: *Nowadays, the only security is social.*

30

THE DEVOTED
OLD COUPLE

The god Hermes, having heard much of the great love which an old couple bore each other and of their kindness to all who came their way, disguised himself as a shabby traveler and appeared at their hut. The old man was at work in his stony field, but the old woman bade the traveler welcome. She brought a basin of water at once so that her visitor might bathe his feet and refresh himself.

Though the couple possessed only enough food for their own needs, the woman cheerfully placed before the traveler her last pitcher of milk and loaf of bread. Hermes ate greedily, but the woman did not rebuke him and apologized that she had no other fare to offer him.

Having thus assured himself that the couple's reputation was fully deserved, Hermes resumed his own divine appearance. The old woman was frightened, but Hermes said, "I have come only to reward you. Would you desire bags of gold? Or shall I make your farm the most productive in Attica?"

But the woman, after much thought, shook her head and said, "No, we have grown content with our lot. Only grant that I may die before my husband, for I could not bear my existence without him."

"Would you not rather I made you a young and beautiful girl again?" asked the god.

"No, only that I may not survive my husband," said the old woman.

"It shall be so," answered Hermes, and vanished.

The woman mentioned nothing of her divine visitor to her husband. But she soon began to worry how the old man would fare without her. So she sought her husband's promise to remarry when she had crossed the river Styx.

But the old man always answered, "You're as tough as oak, so there's still plenty of time to discuss such matters. Anyway, I'm too old to put up with a strange woman in our house. Besides, what good would an old man like me be to a woman?"

"There's plenty that would be glad to have a kind husband and a pleasant little farm," his wife would argue. "You'll need someone to look after you. Who'd cook your meals? Who'd bring you a pitcher of cold spring water and make you rest a moment from the heat when you've been working in the field?"

In this vein, the wife nagged at her husband, giving him not a moment's peace until finally the old man consented to marry again. But then the old woman found fresh cause to worry. After much consideration, she went to her husband and said, "I still shall not be able to die content until I have made a will. Go, then, to the town and bring back a scribe to record my wishes."

"A will!" exclaimed the husband, convinced his wife

had taken leave of her senses. "Dear wife, you've nothing to bestow but a few pots and pans." But the woman insisted so strongly that at last the man went for the scribe.

Closeting herself alone with the scribe, the old woman commanded, "Write down that it's all for my dear husband. My selfish relatives are to have nothing. And if the good soul has sense enough to remarry, then his wife shall have all my cherished possessions—my Phoenician silver pins, my tortoise-shell comb set with stones of lapis lazuli and my gold wedding band."

No sooner had the scribe taken his departure when Hermes appeared before the old woman. "Why have you made a false will?" demanded the angry god. "You are only a poor farmer's wife and you possess none of the fine things you've set down in your will for your successor."

"What else should I do?" asked the poor woman. "My faithless husband has given his word to remarry. But now his wife will never cease plaguing him for the treasures she thinks I've bequeathed her. With any luck at all, it'll only take a month until Charon ferries my old man across the Styx to join me."

MORAL: *Love and diamonds come mixed with clay.*

31

THE WOLF
AND THE STORK

One day a wolf, who never had had much success at fishing, unexpectedly caught a large and juicy salmon in the river. In his greed, the wolf forgot the care with which fish should be eaten and gobbled the salmon so hastily that he succeeded in lodging a sharp bone in his throat.

In great pain, and fearing that each breath would be his last, the wolf ran for help. But none of the other animals wished to aid the suffering wolf, even though he promised to reward them. Finally a stork took pity on the desperate animal and agreed to be of service.

Inserting his long and narrow beak down the wolf's throat, the stork was able to reach the fish bone and remove it. When the wolf again was able to breathe comfortably, the stork requested his promised reward. "I trust you will be generous," said the stork to the wolf.

"It was a delicate and difficult operation, which a professional surgeon, I daresay, could not have performed better."

To this the wolf gave answer, "My dear friend, are you not content that you were able to remove your own head safely from between a wolf's jaws? That should be reward enough for you."

The stork, who really had not expected the wolf to keep his promise anyway, flew away without argument, leaving the wolf quite pleased with his own wit in cheating the stork.

Unfortunately for the wolf, however, his narrow escape from death awakened an infantile memory of how his mother had saved him and his fellow cubs from a pack of hunting dogs only at the cost of her own life. The wolf subconsciously merged the stork, a common maternity symbol, into his mother image.

This created guilt feelings in the wolf, which expressed themselves typically in the form of an anxiety neurosis. Among the wolf's neurotic symptoms was a severe sore throat, which prevented him from eating a morsel of food or swallowing more than a few drops of water. And while this gave the wolf the subconscious satisfaction of expiating his guilt, it also resulted a few days later in his lingering death from starvation.

MORAL: *To thine own self be true, and thou canst then be false to any man.*

32

THE EAGLE AND
THE ARCHER

Possessing a common interest in hunting, an eagle and an archer became close companions. The eagle often spied out game for the archer, and the archer, for his part, generously shared his spoils with the eagle.

One day the archer fashioned a new bow, the finest he had ever made, together with a score of excellent arrows. He hastened to the eagle to display his handicraft. When the eagle complimented the archer on his new weapon, the archer said, "Ah, if I only could obtain feathers worthy of the arrow shafts."

At this, the eagle insisted on providing the archer with quills by plucking feathers from his own wings.

Not long after, the archer saw the eagle circling in the sky and, tempted by the rare beauty of the target, loosed an arrow at the great bird. The arrow lodged in the eagle's breast and he fell to earth, dead, much to the grief of the impulsive archer.

MORAL: *It's the self-inflicted wounds that prove fatal.*

33

THE LION AND
THE FARMER

An emotionally unstable lion believed himself in love with the daughter of a farmer. So he went to the farmer for permission to court the farm maid.

Having a lion for a son-in-law was not a pleasing prospect for the farmer, but he did not dare to anger the great beast. So he cunningly said to the lion, "Your large and sharp teeth would frighten my daughter. To be frank, they even make me nervous. Take my advice and have them removed before you come wooing."

"Even if I have to live on mush the rest of my life, I'll do it!" exclaimed the love-demented lion. And as soon as all his teeth were extracted, the lion returned.

"I don't like to make personal criticisms," said the farmer, "but it's really for your own good. Your claws are too menacing to permit romantic feelings to flower in a girl's bosom."

"It'll feel strange without claws," said the lion. "But if you really think it will improve my chances, then I'm off to have them pulled."

So the lion had all his claws pulled, and when he was able to walk again, he went back to the farmer. But the farmer, seeing the lion shorn of his natural weapons, beat the lion with a club and chased him off the premises.

Back in the jungle, all the other lions laughed at him, and even the mice felt it safe to sneer at him. So the lion committed suicide by jumping off a cliff into a river swarming with crocodiles.

MORAL: *Free advice is worth its price.*

34

HOW THE
ANIMALS FOUND
A JUDGE

Tiring of their perpetual strife, all the animals of the jungle agreed to choose a judge who would settle their differences peaceably. But when they met to select one of their number for this task, they encountered difficulty.

First they asked the elephant to be judge, for he was widely respected by reason of his intelligence. But the elephant refused, saying, "I'm afraid I'm too softhearted to visit punishment upon even the worst of wrong-doers."

The animals next asked the lion to serve, since all stood in awe of the lion's sternness and great strength. But the lion begged off, saying, "I'm not wise enough to tell right from wrong for my own guidance, let alone for others."

So the animals then asked a very learned owl to become their lawgiver. But the owl replied, "Being so wise that I find perplexities and complications in all matters, it would take me years to render a decision in even the simplest dispute."

Seeing his chance in this state of affairs, a jackal came forward. "I am fully qualified to be your judge," said the jackal, "for I am neither goodhearted, strong, nor wise. True, I have a large and hungry family I should look after, but my wish to serve the general welfare has overcome my concern for my own interests. If you insist upon it, I will hold the office."

Lacking any other candidate, the animals agreed to make the jackal their judge, even though many had doubts about his fitness. Unfortunately, once the jackal was in office, he showed that he cared nothing about the issues that were brought before him but only for the honors that he considered were due his position.

So the animals again took counsel with each other, seeking a judge who would be more interested in his duties. But again those most qualified were reluctant to serve. Only an ape, who thought it would be amusing to meddle in the affairs of the other animals, offered to replace the jackal. And as the animals felt that he could not possibly be worse than the jackal, they elected the ape.

But the ape's judgments were so mischievous that matters soon were worse than before. Thereupon the animals retired the ape and re-elected the jackal. In this fashion, the ape and the jackal continued to succeed each other in office whenever the animals were freshly outraged by the one or the other.

MORAL: *Democracy is pretty complicated.*

35
THE DONKEY
AND THE
LAP DOG

On his return from a journey, an itinerant peddler brought his wife a small lap dog. The good woman welcomed her husband's gift warmly, playing with the dog all day and stuffing him with delicacies.

Seeing the favored treatment given the dog, the peddler's donkey became jealous. He grumbled to himself, "I have always carried my master's heavy load of wares without complaint. Yet my only reward is a straw bed in the stable and a handful of fodder. It is clear that around here honest work means less than winsome ways."

So the donkey entered the house, jumped onto his mistress's lap and brayed endearingly. The poor woman not only was frightened out of her wits but received bruises that remained black-and-blue for weeks. Instead of delicacies, the donkey received such a beating with a heavy stick that he nearly died.

MORAL: *A lap dog is a lap dog is a lap dog.*

36

THE FARMER
AND THE FOX

A farmer, who had been dominated for many years by his wife, trapped the fox who had been doing much damage to his barnyard. "You won't get off with a quick death, my sly friend," said the farmer. After giving much

thought to a suitable punishment for the fox, the farmer soaked a cloth in kerosene, tied it securely to the fox's tail and set fire to the cloth. Then the farmer freed the fox so that he might enjoy the creature's desperate flight.

But the fox ran into the farmer's ripe wheat fields, setting fire to the crop, so the farmer saw his entire harvest destroyed before his eyes. The farmer was grief-stricken and remained so for years, especially because his wife continually reminded him the whole thing was all his own fault.

MORAL: *Among the stupid, cruelty serves as wit.*

37

THE MISER WHO
WAS ROBBED OF
HIS GOLD

Once there was a miser in Athens who exchanged all that he earned for gold. He melted the gold into lumps which he then painted the color of stones in order to deceive thieves. These he stored in a chest which he buried in a secret place. But whenever the opportunity presented itself, the miser would dig up the chest to gloat over his wealth.

A thief, who heard of the miser's habit of buying gold but never spending any, kept a careful watch until he learned where the treasure was hidden. Then the thief dug up the chest and made off with its contents.

Upon discovering that his hoard had been stolen, the miser tore his garments and filled the air with his cries of anguish. The wind carried his cries to Mount Olympus, where Zeus became curious about the cause of the man's lamentations. Transforming himself into the guise of a cattle trader, Zeus appeared before the miser.

"How much gold do you require to provide for your wife and children?" asked Zeus, thinking to replace the stolen hoard.

"I have neither wife nor children," replied the wretched man. "I can't afford matrimony."

"Did you use the gold for yourself, then?"

"Never. The gold was only for storing," said the miser.

"I doubt that the thief can be found or your gold restored," said Zeus. "But it is not necessary to grieve on that account, for you can easily find stones that will serve you as well as your gold. Fondle the stones to your heart's content, they will never tell you they are not gold."

The miser cursed Zeus for his counsel, counting it foolish, and continued to lament for his vanished treasure. But one day he found a stone that so much resembled one of his lumps of gold that he placed it in his chest. Thereafter, whenever he found a suitable stone, he added it to his collection.

Gloating over his rocks instead of gold, the miser became much interested in mineralogy, geology, and related sciences. In time, he became a paleontologist, a mild obsession that created much less social envy than his earlier mania. He was welcome among his neighbors, and even Socrates came to hear his lectures on fossils and rocks.

MORAL: *Symbols can be purchased but status must be earned.*

38
THE WOLF
IN SHEEP'S CLOTHING

A young wolf, who had transvestite tendencies and took pleasure in dressing himself unusually, came upon a sheepskin. He put it on immediately and ran home to show his parents how lovely it made him look.

"Take that stupid thing off at once!" growled the father wolf.

"It looks silly on you, dear," said the mother wolf more gently.

Reluctant to part with his sheepskin, the young wolf said, "It may look funny to you, but it will look familiar to the shepherd and his dogs. Disguised by this costume, I can fool them and slip in with the sheep. We'll be able to dine on lamb as often as we like."

"Say, that's pretty clever," said the father admiringly. "You've got a head on your shoulders, youngster."

"Our little cub is turning out to be a fine wolf," said the mother proudly.

So the wolf, masquerading as a sheep, joined the nearest flock. The shepherd assumed only that a stray had returned and paid no further attention to the disguised wolf.

But the wolf reasoned to himself, "They're probably suspicious of me. I'd best behave like a real sheep for a while." So the wolf grazed on the meadow, played with the lambs in their simple games, and huddled together with the sheep at night.

After a few days, the wolf noticed that grass tasted sweeter than meat and that sheep were really more intelligent than they looked. And though his father and mother were dreadfully upset, the wolf stayed with the sheep for the rest of his life.

MORAL: *A strong pretense is the best defense.*

39

THE OLD MAN
AND HIS MISTRESS

Approaching the golden sunset of his life, a man
found himself indifferent to the charms of his wife. So
he took a young woman as his mistress. On learning of
this, the wife took every opportunity to pluck her hus-

band's remaining black hairs, in order that his mirror might remind him that he was too old for such folly.

On the other hand, the young mistress was ashamed of having an old man for a lover, so she employed every chance to pull out his gray hairs. In a short while, the two women between them made the man completely bald.

MORAL: *There is no cure for baldness.*

40

THE DOG
WITH A BONE

A dog was crossing a bridge with a bone between his jaws when he noticed his own reflection in the water below. Not content with the one bone, he greedily desired the bone which the reflection also held in its jaws.

He barked ferociously, thinking to make the other dog abandon its bone, but instead the bone he was carrying fell into the water and was lost.

Noticing that his actions were duplicated by the reflection, the dog realized that he was observing his own image. Greatly taken by his own appearance, he said to himself, "I never before saw how handsome I was. What clear, intelligent eyes! Notice, if you please, the aristocratic lineage indicated by that noble forehead! And how those strong jaws bespeak my strength of character!"

Anxious to study his features in greater detail, he leaned further and further over the bridge until he fell into the water and was drowned.

MORAL: *Reflect before you genuflect.*

41

THE CITY MOUSE
AND THE
COUNTRY MOUSE

A little country mouse, who had been the puniest of his litter and who had compensated for his infantile inadequacy by developing an aggressive personality, was visited one day by his cousin, a city mouse. As he served his guest supper, the country mouse said belligerently, "I suppose you won't find my humble fare much to your liking. But gleanings of barley and corn agree with me. The tough kernels are good for my teeth and they supply in nutrition what they lack in flavor."

"Very wholesome, indeed," agreed the city mouse.

"Besides," continued the country mouse, "the air out here is fresh and wholesome, uncontaminated by gasoline fumes and automobile exhaust. And the peace and quiet of the countryside will do more for your nerves than a bottle of tranquilizers."

"Right again," said the city mouse. "The rural atmosphere does produce a sense of calm and emotional stability. In fact, I'm thinking of moving away from the city, which is why I came to visit you."

"Really?" asked the country mouse, astonished. "I certainly would like to see the big city for myself."

"Why not stay with me for a few days?" suggested the city mouse. "But I tell you that although the big city is a fine place to visit, you won't like living there."

So the country mouse accompanied his cousin back to his home, a duplex penthouse shared with a wealthy family. In his turn as host, the city mouse served a supper of cold lobster and shrimp, smoked fish, turkey, roast beef, four kinds of imported cheese, assorted vegetables, seven varieties of bread and rolls, a choice of French pastry, sherbet, or ice cream for dessert, followed by salted nuts and after-dinner mints.

"Boy, this is some party!" exclaimed the country mouse. "What a feed!"

"Oh, this is no party," said the city mouse. "This is how we dine every day. In fact, I'm a little chagrined the family failed to serve champagne tonight, so we shall have to do without wine."

"And you want to give up living like this to move to the sticks?" asked the country mouse incredulously.

"There's a catch to it, which you'll see any second now," said the city mouse bitterly. At that moment, a big overfed cat appeared and the city mouse squeaked, "Run for your life!"

Panting in his hole, the city mouse said to his cousin, "See what I mean? How can you relax and enjoy your dinner when a cat is always prowling around? And my family also keeps a Pekingese, who must bite dreadfully, to judge by his bark."

"Have an after-dinner mint," said the country mouse cheerfully. "I grabbed a pawful as we left."

"Then there's the exterminator," added the city mouse. "He's always putting traps and strychnine nuggets in the most out-of-the-way places. You have to keep your wits about you every moment, I warn you—there's no absent-minded nibbling at some stray piece of Italian salami or an unexpected bit of caviar, as you value your life. Oh, it's a dreadful strain on the nerves!"

"Say, why don't we dash out, spit in the cat's eye and jump back in the hole? It would be fun to make that smug Siamese simmer," said the country mouse.

"Don't do that!" cried his cousin, "she'd never forgive the insult. Pray sit still and don't utter a sound. She'll tire of waiting after a while."

"Personally, I think it adds a lot of zest to a meal to know you're simultaneously annoying a cat, disturbing a dog, and worrying an exterminator," said the country mouse happily.

So the city mouse and the country mouse exchanged homes and each lived happily thereafter in his new environment.

MORAL: *Competition, like virtue, is its own reward.*

42

THE VIPER
AND THE WASP

A well-adjusted, emotionally stable viper who had always enjoyed his life was bullied into a dispute with an abnormally aggressive wasp. The vicious insect decided to teach the snake a lesson, so he secured a hold behind the snake's head, where he began stinging his adversary without respite. The viper frantically resorted to every contortion and maneuver he could perform, but he was not able to dislodge the merciless wasp.

In desperation, the snake took himself and his unwelcome guest to a well-traveled road and lay in the wheel tracks. In a moment, a wagon came along, crushing both the snake and his relentless enemy.

MORAL: *A smart parasite quits when he's ahead.*

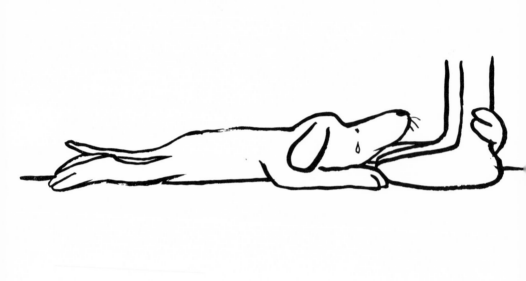

43

THE AILING
FARM DOG

A farm dog was stricken with a severe and painful attack of asthma, but was reluctant to inform his master for fear of being put to death as old and useless. So the dog sought instead the help of an owl renowned for his knowledge of natural medicine.

"Once, when I ate too many field mice," said the owl, "I had an attack like yours. Just stop eating mice for a week or two and you will recover promptly."

"But I never eat mice," replied the dog. "My duties include killing all the mice I encounter, but I dislike their flavor."

"Then that must be it," said the owl. "You should eat at least three a day. But be sure to eat them whole, with fur, tail and all. I always do and my health could not be better."

The dog sought to follow the owl's advice but found the remedy so unpleasant that he decided to seek a fresh opinion from an aged squirrel famous for his energy and agility.

"You don't get enough exercise," said the squirrel. "Climb the highest tree you can find and spend the day leaping from branch to branch. You'll feel better at once."

"But I've never been able to climb even a small tree," replied the dog.

"Then you'd best begin now if you value your health," said the squirrel, and scampered off to follow his own advice.

The dog made an honest effort to climb a small tree, but he only wrenched his back. So he went to a wise barnyard rooster for better counsel. "I suffered a case of severe croup very analogous to your asthma," said the rooster. "It came on immediately following my shameful discovery that one of the hens in my flock was my own mother. You see, asthma is the physiological equivalent of crying, crying for the guilt you feel sub-consciously. The only cure is to give up your affair with your mother."

"My mother has been dead for many years," answered the dog sadly. "And unless I am given a prescription which it is possible for me to follow, it will not be long before I join her."

Despairing of his life, the dog had no alternative but to beg his master to send for the veterinarian. His master was sitting on the porch in a rocking chair, eating a light snack of goat cheese and olives before supper and watching his hired hands at work in the fields. "Veterinarian indeed!" exclaimed the master, on hearing his dog's complaint. "I can tell you what's wrong with you, you fat loafer. You eat too much and work too little. I shall put you on a diet of water and find some heavier tasks for you."

After a week of strenuous labor without so much as a morsel of food, the dog died, greatly to his own relief.

MORAL: *Always look for a doctor who has your disease.*

44

THE FROG
AND THE OX

A frog and her children once were crossing a meadow when they encountered an ox. The vastness of the ox caused much excitement among the little frogs, but the very youngest of the frogs said, "Our mother could be as big as the ox if she chose to. It's just that she prefers a size more commensurate with our own."

This immediately caused an argument among the siblings, some of whom were skeptical while others maintained their mother could do anything. Finally the youngest frog begged his mother to settle the stubborn dispute.

Moved by the childish faith in her, the mother frog said, "Oh, it's simple enough for a frog to swell up by sucking in air. It's just that I've never applied myself to such a large model. I daresay it won't be too difficult. Just tell me when I reach the proper size."

So the frog began swallowing air and puffing herself up, while the little frogs croaked their encouragement. Taking one breath too many, the frog burst, simultaneously exploding herself and her children's mother image.

MORAL: *If you're too big for your britches, get another pair.*

45

THE WOLF
AND THE LAMB

A wolf, who had suffered excessively from sibling rivalry when a cub, once caught a lamb that had strayed from the flock. Instead of dispatching his prey immediately, the wolf sought a preliminary gratification by tormenting the animal.

First the wolf pretended he was about to kill the lamb, but he only bit the lamb's fleece. Then, seating himself in the shade of a tree, the wolf ordered the lamb to entertain him by telling some spicy stories or singing an obscene song. When the lamb admitted she did not know such stories or songs, the wolf produced his flute and ordered the lamb to dance to his music.

Attracted by the sound of the flute, the shepherd went to the scene with his dogs to investigate and promptly killed the wolf. But the lamb said to the shepherd, "Who asked you to intervene? I was a little frightened at first by his rough manners. But it was easy to see he liked me, and we were just beginning to have fun when you had to spoil things."

MORAL: *For every sadist, somewhere there's a masochist waiting.*

46

THE FOXES
AND THE HARES

An ambitious family named Fox, upon moving to a select suburb, was not satisfied with this improvement in its social standing but was intent on achieving membership in the community's exclusive country club. For this purpose, the Foxes exhibited the warmest and friendliest of behavior, entertaining incessantly and overlooking no stratagem to ingratiate themselves.

The father went from one neighbor to another, generously using his time to teach this one how to improve his golf game and that one how to grow a greener lawn. The mother often stayed up half the night making elaborate hors d'oeuvres and canapés for every community affair, and with pretended cheerfulness gave her old family recipe for spice cake to every woman who asked for it. The son, who attended college, brought his classmates home for all the girls in the neighborhood

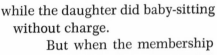

while the daughter did baby-sitting without charge.

But when the membership committee of the country club met, their comment was not favorable. "The Foxes think they know it all," said one member. "They're always putting on airs," added the other member. "They're really condescending snobs," decided the chairman.

"There's a much nicer family, by the name of Hare, that just moved out my way," said the first member. "I met the father when he came to ask my advice about his roses. A timid but steady sort, I thought."

"My wife took to the mother right away," added the other member. "Not much of a cook, though. She had to ask my wife how to make a roast beef."

"The club would mean a lot to them," decided the chairman. "Their girl begged my daughter to help her meet some boys."

So the first family was rejected, but the second family was welcomed into the country club.

MORAL: *Inferiority is the mother of conformity and the father isn't much better, either.*

47

THE FARM HAND
AND THE VIPER

A farm hand was walking along a snowy road in the dead of winter when he came across a viper, stiff with cold and all but dead. Feeling pity for the serpent, he picked it up, opened his sheepskin coat and placed it against his chest to warm.

The farm hand hardly had reached his hut when the viper, warmed back to life, sank his fangs into the farm hand's breast. Knowing the bite was fatal, the farm hand cried out, "Witness, O gods of Olympus, how my act of mercy has been rewarded. Ah, but you rule mankind badly!"

The Physician God, Apollo, heard these bitter reproaches and instantly appeared before the man. "Do not regret your compassion for the lowly snake," said Apollo. "I shall not permit you to die in consequence of your kindness but shall heal your wound and render the venom harmless."

"Thank you," said the astonished farm hand. "But I really didn't mean to complain. After all, I brought my death upon myself."

"That is very manly of you," replied Apollo. "Still, you should not suffer death because of a merciful impulse."

"I respect your good intentions," argued the farm hand, "but do you think it right to come between a man and his fate? On principle, it seems wrong for the gods to meddle in the affairs of men."

While Apollo was still trying to prevail upon the farm hand to accept his beneficent offer, the man fell dead.

MORAL: *If he can't help himself, you can't either—and if he can, why should you bother?*

48

THE WATCHDOG
AND THE FOX

A watchdog and a fox, meeting by chance in the forest, struck up a conversation. But when they spoke of their daily existence, the dog expressed his dissatisfaction. "Why, I get nothing to eat but table scraps, and in none too generous an amount at that," complained the dog. "You, however, eat what you like, when it pleases you, and to the limits of your appetite. If it's a bit of fresh fruit or berries you hanker for, you have only to reach out. When you fancy an egg for your breakfast, then you take your fill from a bird's nest. As for the meat you eat, it's always freshly killed to your order and doubtless most flavorsome."

"That is true enough," said the fox. "Indeed, I never realized that things could be otherwise for any creature. But what is that strange line around your neck where the hair has been rubbed off?"

"Oh, that comes of wearing the collar which my master fastens around my neck," answered the dog. "He wishes to make certain that I'm at hand every evening and attending to my duty."

"Then you cannot decide for yourself each evening whether to stay home or to wander off in quest of adventure?" asked the fox.

"Certainly not," declared the dog. "My master rules me in that as well as in all other matters. Indeed, he even presumes to choose my mates for me without consulting my tastes or ascertaining my wishes."

"How lucky you are," exclaimed the fox, "to have someone willing to make such vexing decisions for you. Each year of my life I have selected a mate and I've never made a good choice yet. Would you consider trading places with me?"

Seeing the matter in a different light, the dog returned home and remained content with his lot.

MORAL: *There's no conformity without some deformity.*

EPILOGUE

In the event the foregoing fables have failed to clear up your emotional disorders and you intend to proceed next to psychoanalysis, the following fable, which is not adapted from Aesop, has been written by Professor Duerf for your particular guidance:

49

THE PRETTY
KLEPTOMANIAC
AND THE
INEXPERIENCED
PSYCHOANALYST

A young woman developed a mania for stealing. At first this compulsion afforded her much gratification, the more so because she thus acquired many expensive accessories she could not have afforded to buy. But when she had several narrow escapes from arrest, she became alarmed by her irresistible impulses. So she went to seek help from a psychoanalyst, by chance choosing one who was young and inexperienced.

Moved by a desire to be of service no less than by the woman's youth and beauty, the psychoanalyst was enthusiastic over prospects for her cure. "Kleptomania is a comparatively simple compulsion," said the analyst. "As soon as we can discover what prevents you from expressing your sexual energies in a more normal fashion, we can free you of this socially undesirable behavior. My fee is thirty-five dollars a session."

Although the young woman was anxious to begin treatment at his hands, she was required to explain that her circumstances made his fee prohibitive. "My dear young lady," answered the psychoanalyst, "your resistance to being helped expresses itself in your resistance to my fee. Your case is more serious, therefore, than I thought." So the pretty patient agreed to both the treatment and the fee.

After many pleasant sessions devoted to discussing her dreams, her childhood memories, and her suppressed erotic desires, the young woman found that her mania had disappeared. Much pleased by the successful outcome of his therapy, the analyst informed the patient she was discharged and sought to collect the payment due him.

But the young woman said, "I was able to pay you before with the proceeds of my thieving. But in curing me, you have also dried up the source of your fee. Can't I repay you in some other way?"

MORAL: *Personality is an incurable disease with variable symptoms.*